BEFORE T

BEFORE THE BLADE

BEFORE
THE
BLADE

What You Need to Know Before Getting Microblading or Semi Permanent Makeup

Hannah L. Maruyama

BEFORE THE BLADE

To my husband, who has taught, challenged, and loved me more than anyone, to my mother and siblings who make me laugh when I was discouraged, to my husband's entire family, who has pulled me in, helped me up, and fed me so much good food, to my friends who love me even though I don't answer my phone, and to my grandfather, who I wish had been able to see this.

CONTENTS

BEFORE THE BLADE

INTRODUCTION

It was sticky, humid, and full of gnats. A pretty average September night in Savannah, Georgia. What wasn't average were the two hours I had spent talking to the woman who had met me to look at a car I had listed on Craigslist. Her name was Eva, and she was a night shift ER nurse and mother of three. She had been considering microblading, semi permanent brows, for almost a year. Eva wanted her brows done because her work and home schedule was hectic, and the idea of waking up feeling ready to leave the house seemed amazing to her.

Her husband had long since gotten back in their car when she told me her grandmother and some of her cousins had their eyebrows done in Miami in the late 70's, she was convinced hers would turn out the same: faded, harsh, and blue! I explained that what her grandmother and cousins had was an actual tattoo, rather than semi permanent makeup, and that's why the brows had aged so poorly (I'll address this in more depth in a later chapter). After laying out this information, she thanked me and as she turned to leave, she off-handedly told me I should write a book.

After some thought and with huge support from my husband, I did just that. And now you're reading it!

I am a semi permanent makeup artist and have found that most people I meet (women and men alike) are either considering or curious about semi permanent make-up. Microblading seems to be picking up speed. Maybe it's because social media (here's looking at you, Instagram) makes information on new beauty science so readily available, but nowadays once people find out what I do for a living, it's all questions! Though I'll admit, I do have fun answering them.

Here are a few of the most frequent:

"Why is it so expensive?"
"How long does it last?"
"Can you look at them before they tattoo them on?"
"Does it hurt?"
"Is it an actual tattoo?"
"Does it look weird up close?"
"Can I still have it done if I have real tattoo eyebrows?"

There is nothing wrong with these questions, but there is something wrong about how many misconceptions there are about semi permanent make-up. Whenever possible, I try to clear up the confusion. This book is for anyone who might want semi permanent makeup and those who currently have it but would like to learn more about other procedures.

When you are finished reading, you will:
- be sure if you do (or don't) qualify for semi permanent makeup
- understand that semi permanent makeup is committing to a beauty investment
- be comfortable choosing an artist and voicing your preferences
- know the difference between semi permanent makeup and permanent makeup
- know the difference between semi permanent makeup and tattoos
- be a fantastic and informed client!

Since many people have complex questions about microblading specifically, this book also provides information on the goals and outcomes, the types of brow microblading, the different procedures involved, and includes what to expect after the procedure.

This book is for everyone interested in semi permanent makeup. Whether you already have some experience with these procedures or are a first-timer who is considering semi permanent makeup but wants to understand the process as well as the risks and commitment involved, this book is for you. In addition, the curious beauty researcher who has been combing the internet only to end up more confused than before they started, will find answers within these pages.

I hope I answer all your questions and provide valuable insight that will help you decide if investing in semi permanent makeup is the right choice for you and your beauty journey.

CHAPTER ONE

Is It Semi Permanent Makeup or Permanent Makeup?

Short answer: both. This topic is controversial in the professional cosmetic tattoo community. Frankly, I don't believe the name means much, as long as you understand what it is.

No matter what it is called, implanting any color into any layer of the skin is a tattoo. By definition, a tattoo is permanent. However, modern 'permanent' makeup is done using pigment, not tattoo ink, and that is why I come down on the side of 'semi permanent' makeup. **It does fade.** Even those belonging to the 'permanent' makeup school of thought acknowledge cosmetic tattoos (using cosmetic tattoo tools and pigment, not ink) fade over time and requires touch ups, while regular tattoos do not (or not nearly as often). As a user and semi permanent makeup artist, I believe you want them to fade. When they fade, you can change them if desired, and that is an option I feel is necessary for beauty practices over all.

Semi Permanent Makeup

Microblading, eyeliner tattoo, beauty mark, freckle tattoos, scar and re-pigmentation tattoos and lip blush tattoos are all semi permanent makeup if they are done with pigments, (not tattoo inks). Pigments are the vehicle for semi permanent makeup. **Pigments are specifically engineered to fade.** They are **DESIGNED** to go away. Semi permanent makeup is applied to the deepest layer of your epidermis (basal). It is semi permanent because the pigment will grow out and slough off with your skin over a period of 6 to 36 months, depending on your skin type, age, metabolism, and amount of exposure to sun.

Permanent Makeup

Permanent makeup is done with a tattoo gun and tattoo ink, and is applied to the dermis which is the layer of skin under the epidermis. It is permanent because the ink is more binding than pigment and it is implanted into the dermis and cannot grow out and slough off with your top layer of skin. Your dermis has more nerve endings and is more vascular that your epidermis, meaning it has more blood vessels, which is why tattoos hurt and bleed more than semi permanent makeup.

Semi permanent makeup, permanent makeup, cosmetic tattooing, micropigmentation, eyebrow embroidery, 2D, 3D, 4D brows – these are different names for the same technical process, as all of these procedures are depositing pigment into breaks in the skin (dermis), and that pigment can't be washed off.

The Difference Between Pigment and Ink

The 'semi' in semi permanent makeup is the pigment. Pigments are now designed to fade naturally and true to color, whereas permanent makeup color used to be titanium dioxide ink, which has much larger particles than semi permanent makeup pigments. The fading of the tattoo ink is the cause of the dreaded greenish blue brows.

Modern semi permanent makeup uses pigments, while tattoos use ink. Pigments are neutral colors found naturally on the human body: browns, pink browns, red browns and flesh tones. **Side note:** (There are unnatural looking variations of pigments that artists use to tone colors according to your skin tone like olive green, grey, or orange. They can also be used as color correction to control the healed outcome of your procedure. If you've ever seen a hair stylists use purple shampoo on bleached blonde hair to tone out orange or brassy color, you've seen color correction in action.) Tattoo inks come in a wide variety of colors like purple, black, bright green and neon yellow which allows tattoo artists to create more vivid tattoos.

Semi permanent makeup pigments contain iron oxide, which is a safe base and considered very stable. Typical tattoo ink is full of chemicals such as mercury sulfide, lead, chromium, nickel, ash, among others. Though it is highly unlikely to have an allergic reaction to tattoo ink, it is even less likely to have one to semi permanent makeup pigment due to the iron oxide and its stability.

Now, to be clear, no pigments or inks are FDA approved for being placed into the skin. Zip, zero, nada. Most semi permanent makeup pigments are FDA approved for cosmetic use, meaning, **on** your skin, not **in** your skin. **There are no FDA approved tattoo pigments or inks of any kind, as they outsource cosmetic tattoo pigment and tattoo ink regulation to local or state governments who often do not add any regulation**. But don't let that stop you from having semi permanent makeup. Most artists strive for great results (they want more business!), and because of that, they use good quality pigments, and if they are using good quality pigments and are licensed, it's extremely unlikely you will have any issues.

CHAPTER TWO

Tools of the Trade

Semi permanent makeup tools are delicate, sterile blades made of 6-18 tiny needles in a row. They look like itty-bitty Exacto knives. Small digital hand tools that are designed for semi permanent makeup application are becoming more widely used as well. They are generally about the length of a fork and about as wide around as big cigar. Though they make a buzzing sound, they are much quieter than a traditional coil tattoo gun. These digital machines have become a staple for semi permanent makeup artists because it can deposit color more evenly to the skin and is much less traumatic to the skin than hand-shading with a blade made of needles. Some clients find the noise intimidating if they have never had a tattoo, but there is no reason to be afraid of it. The benefit of a digital rotary gun is that your brows will heal a bit better and your semi permanent makeup will probably stay put longer, meaning you can go longer in between touch-up appointments. **(More bang for your buck!)**

Good semi permanent makeup artists use disposable tools. Gloves, single use blades, needle cartridges, numbing applicators, pigment containers, gauze, and medical pads make the risk of cross contamination and blood-borne diseases less than that of a traditional tattoo. However, there is an ever present risk for HIV or Hepatitis because of the open cuts and bleeding. **Make sure you**

disclose any blood-borne diseases to your artist. It protects you, them, and others.

CHAPTER THREE

Who Should Have Semi permanent Makeup

Everyone!

Guys, gals, young, old! If you don't have any health or conditions that would make semi permanent makeup risky for you, it's a wide open world. There are an ever-increasing number of skilled artists learning and developing amazing semi permanent makeup procedures!

People who have lost their hair due to cancer treatment or alopecia often use semi permanent makeup to repair or cover their hair loss. It is also fantastic for seniors who have lost the sight or dexterity they need to apply their makeup or those with physical disabilities for who have trouble applying.

Who Can't Have Semi permanent Makeup

Semi permanent makeup can be a huge help to those who have lost their hair due to chemo therapy, age, or alopecia. But if you have a serious health condition or disease, make sure you check with your doctor before having any semi permanent makeup done. Some artists may require a note from a doctor if your health issue is serious or chronic. If any of the following conditions or circumstances apply, you should not have semi permanent makeup done:

- are sunburned
- have liver disease
- have diabetes ***unless a doctor's note can be obtained**
- are subject to developing keloid (raised and expanding) scars
- have broken or infected skin (i.e. active cold sores or cuts)
- have a cold or flu ***wait until you are healed**
- had Botox or a chemical peel in the last six months
- been on Accutane in the last six months
- have a heart conditions or are on heart or blood pressure medication
- have active cold sores
- are pregnant or breastfeeding
- have had an organ transplant ***unless a doctor's note can be obtained**
- are currently going through chemotherapy ***unless a doctor's note can be obtained**
- get keloid or hypertrophic scarring
- have lip fillers ***this can cause lip blush tattoo results to be unpredictable**
- have glaucoma ***specifically for eyeliner**
- have an auto immune disease (some auto immune diseases are fine, but your healing time is typically longer than normal) *ask your doctor then your artist!

CHAPTER FOUR

Types of Semi permanent Makeup Procedures

As mentioned in Chapter 2, there are many kinds of semi permanent makeup procedures that can be done all over the face and body, such as the ones listed below.

Eyebrows

Microblading:

Microblading is currently the most popular semi permanent brow method. It is done using a tiny blade hand tool or an electric pen to create small hair strokes following a pattern within the shape you and the artist have mapped out to match your unique face shape. It looks natural, but should only be performed on those who have relatively normal skin; otherwise your natural skin oil (sebum) will cause it to fade quickly.

This procedure feels like: a sunburn being scratched.

(I have performed microblading on myself, I would have microblading done, and I offer microblading.)

Nano Brows:

Nano brows is microblading, but finer. Even thinner blades result in an even finer hair stroke. Microblades are 0.20mm to 0.28mm thick. Nano blades are 0.12mm to 0.19mm.

Small needles, big difference.

This procedure feels like: a sunburn being scratched.

(I would have nano blading done on myself and I offer nano blading.)

Microfeathering/Microstroking:

This method is done using a hand tool with a tiny blade. The artist fills in the gaps of healthy, relatively full brows with hair strokes. It is more natural looking, but you must have a fair amount of hair in order for this technique to work. Your artist will not let you choose this service unless your brows are thick enough.

This procedure feels like: a sunburn being scratched.

(I would have microfeathering done on myself and I offer microfeathering/microstroking.)

Combination Brows:

Combination brows have microblading strokes done with a manual hand tool at the front of the brow and shading at the bottom and the back of the brow. They are a good choice for someone who wants microblading, but has sparse brows or oily skin. They last longer than microbladed brows.

This procedure feels like: a sunburn being scratched and then poked with a sharp object. Slightly more painful, but also more worth the pain.

(I would have combination brows done on myself and I offer combination brows. **They are my favorite brow type as they look natural but typically last longer than microblading and are a great option for covering up old or botched brows – versatility for the win.**)

Ombre Brows:

Semi permanent ombre brows are done using two shades of pigment, lighter at the front and top and darker at the bottom and back. They look more like makeup brows, when compared to microblading, but help brows look fuller.

This procedure feels like: a sunburn being poked and scraped.

(I would have ombre brows done on myself and I offer ombre brows.)

Powder Brows:

Powder brows are basically ombre brows except they are done using less shading on the top and front instead of a lighter color. A combination brow is a powder brow with some microblading at the front of the brow. Sometimes artists label ombre brow services as powder brows or label ombre brow services as powder brows. Make sure you clarify which service they are referring to, if you prefer one outcome over the other.

This procedure feels like: a sunburn being poked and scraped.

(I would have powder brows done on myself and I offer powder brows.)

Eyes

Semi Permanent Eyeshadow :

Semi permanent eyeshadow has made a huge comeback in Europe. Many artists do a precise fading technique, but I feel strongly that semi permanent eyeshadow is unwise. It's difficult to predict the wear on the shadow from your eyes opening and closing, and you will be stuck with the same shadow, which you may not like if you change your makeup, are exposed to more or less sun, or it goes out of style.

(I would not have semi permanent eyeshadow done, and I would not perform semi permanent eyeshadow.)

Semi Permanent Eyeliner:

Semi permanent eyeliner can be one of the best procedures out there. It keeps liner from smudging all over your lids, from drying out your eyes, allows those with allergies to have liner, is fantastic for older clients whose hands are no longer steady enough to apply liner, and lets you get out of bed looking awake. It also heals faster than other semi permanent makeup, in about 5-7 days after application.

That being said, I will not do extreme winged eyeliner. It is nearly impossible to remove semi permanent eyeliner because of its proximity to your eye and how delicate the skin is. If your eyes sag slightly, or styles change, you will not be happy with it.

(I have performed semi permanent liner on myself, I would have semi permanent liner done, and I do offer semi permanent liner.)

Dark Circle Cover Up:

This is a newer development to semi permanent makeup. A few months ago I saw this trend surface in a video. But it was a tattoo artist, not a SPMUA, offering this, so I am concerned this service is largely done with tattoo ink. Dark circle cover up is done when an artist matches your skin tone and tattoos over dark circles. It can make you look younger, but it's hard to say how long it lasts and there is the possibility of pigment moving into other parts of your face over time. This pigment migration is difficult to predict and it can end up looking patchy and uneven, and you would still have to cover up your dark circles. This application of semi permanent makeup is relatively new, so if you decide to have it, I would encourage you to make sure you are going to a SPMUA and not a tattoo artist.

(I do not think I would have this done, and I do not perform this procedure at this time.)

Lash Line Enhancement:

A lash line enhancement is a delicate tattoo in between your eyelashes. It makes your lashes appear darker and makes your eyes appear larger. There is a small chance of pigment migrating if the artist is inexperienced and does not perform it correctly, but that rarely happens.

(I have done this procedure on myself, I would have it done, and I do perform it.)

Lips

Lip Liner:

Lip liner tattoo has evolved since it became popular decades ago. The modern semi permanent version of lip liner is shaded from the outside to the inside, creating a more natural enhancement of the lip line. If the natural lip shade is not matched well, lip product will still need to be worn. This is a good procedure for those whose lips have lost pigment on their lip border due to aging.

(I would have this done and I do perform this procedure.)

Lip Blush Tattoo:

A lip blush tattoo is the opposite of a lip liner. The shading goes from the inside of your lips and gradually becomes lighter towards the edges. This is generally for younger clients or people who have strong lip borders but would like to make their lips brighter or more vibrant.

(I would have this done and I do not perform this procedure at this time.)

Face

Blush Tattoo:
You can get semi permanent blush, however, it is a large area, and often the resulting color is not what the client wants. It can also migrate and spread throughout your cheeks. If you wear foundation it will be covered up and you will still have to apply blush, making the process of getting the tattoo pointless.

(I would not have this procedure done and I would not perform it.)

Beauty Mark:
Semi permanent beauty marks are simple to do. But they come in and out of style fairly often. Getting a beauty mark is actually a large change, and the placement is extremely important. If it's not exactly where you want it, it will look strange and unnatural and you will be stuck with it. I would advise you to draw one on every day for a month to see if you still like where it is, the size, and the color. Remember: it is going to fade, and it can look like a speck of food, a dirt smudge, or a pimple if not maintained.

(I would not have this procedure done but I would perform it if the client was sure.)

Freckles:
Semi permanent freckles on someone without freckles can be done. Keep in mind that not all of the freckles will stay, nor will they fade at the same rate. Your facial skin gets worn and damaged in different spots, like the sun on the right side of your face during a commute, or from sleeping on your left side and having your face in

a pillow. If you already have freckles and want more, remember that you can't control where you get more freckles, and they can develop too closely to the tattooed freckles making the end result look unnatural. You could end up with large splotchy freckles, not cute little round ones.

(I would not have this procedure done and I would not perform it.)

CHAPTER FIVE

All about Brows

The method of putting color into cuts in the skin is a tattoo method that has been used for centuries all over the globe, but the trend of using this technique on the eyebrows originated in Asia, specifically Korea, and was initially referred to as eyebrow embroidery.

Microblading

Culturally speaking, the last few decades have been rough on women's natural eyebrows. Excessive plucking and waxing has left many women with damaged hair follicles and balding brows. When the full, natural look came back to the forefront, the solutions came in many forms. Powder, pencil, brow gel, even fake eyebrow extensions: all temporary, all time consuming, all easy to mess up and quick to melt off. The most effective way to replace sparse brows with thick healthy ones came in the form of the semi permanent makeup procedures, most commonly, microblading.

The term microblading has also come to encompass other kinds of semi permanent brow methods, like combination, powder, or ombre. But specifically, microblading is using a tiny needle blade to create hair stroke tattoos in the upper layers of skin and fill them with cosmetic pigment, partially or entirely camouflaging missing hair on the eyebrows. It is often combined with other methods like powder brows to make the brows last longer.

Microblading: A Technical Breakdown

Microblading is a semi permanent technique through which itty-bitty hair-like cuts are made and a pigment (thicker than ink) is gently pushed into those cuts in the basal layer of the epidermis (bottom section of the top layer of your skin) to enhance, create or restructure the brows, resulting in fuller, more natural looking brows. There are two main methods; manual or digital pen.

The manual technique uses a super-fine pen like tool (typically a bundle of 12 to 15 needles arranged in a straight line) to put the pigment into the skin. The blades are so small and the cuts they make are so thin and fine that they look like hair. There are varying thickness of these needles, and the thinner the needles, the thinner the result.

The digital pen method uses a small, electric rotary pen with disposable needle cartridges. These needles are usually more delicate than the manual blades, are set in the top of the pen, and used to gently insert the pigment under the skin. The digital technique requires a slightly different skill set, and it is faster. Some people argue this method is less painful than the blade. Artists have begun to favor the digital pen over the manual method because it causes less trauma to the skin.

After the initial procedure, a touch up is **almost always** necessary within eight weeks. The reason for this is that your artist needs to make sure the pigment was applied correctly for your skin type. If it faded a lot, your artist may use a darker pigment to compensate for your skin's response. Often the cost of the touch up is budgeted into the initial service fee to make it easier on you and the artist.

However, some artists may charge for the touch up service separately. Be sure to check your artist's pricing structure.

Semi permanent brows typically cost between **$200 to $3000**, depending on the artist. I'd advise a quick Google search to find average pricing for your area. Brows in New York City are going to be priced differently than brows in a small town in Indiana.

A tip on tipping: I only mention this as it seems there is some uncertainty as to whether or not this is required or expected. Someone even asked me if it was rude to tip a semi permanent makeup artist. I do understand the confusion, so I'll clear it up here.

It is customary to tip your artist the same way you would a hair stylist. If you are a regular, like the work, and plan to return, then I'd suggest a 10-20% tip. Most artists don't expect anything. They are professionals and are being paid for a service. I am always pleasantly surprised when I'm tipped, but never disappointed if I'm not. Go with your gut on this one.

Microbladed brows can last from 6 to 36 months depending on environmental, procedural or personal lifestyle factors. If you are in the sun often or sweat a lot, you will have to get more touch ups than the average person. You should not use retinol and glycolic acid after having your brows done. In time, they will remove the top layer of your skin and the pigment along with it, and you'll be back to square one.

MICROBLADING PROCEDURE: BEGINNING TO END

You think you'd like to get your brows done.

You start to search online, study photos.

You read every Google review you can dig up on the SPMUAs in your area, pick one, and then change your mind twice before changing it back.

You call or text or book online, and make an appointment.

The artist calls you for a phone consultation, asks you to come in prior, or emails you instructions based on your appointment info.

(Keep in mind, if you have old or botched permanent makeup, there will usually be a greater cost and time commitment to fix or refresh your work.)
You are given a set of instructions.

Follow them.

There is nothing worse than giving a list of incredibly specific instructions only to have a client come in, waste their appointment and time, and then have to reschedule because they waxed their eyebrows too close to their microblading appointment. When you come in for your appointment, you will have to sign consent waivers, likely a photo release for your before and after photos, and fill out a medical questionnaire, if you have not already.

You will be asked to lay or sit on the table or chair the artist uses for their procedures. Ask about a pillow for your legs if you have back pain or circulation issues. There will be a bright light shining on your face for a couple hours, so if you are prone to migraines, take this into account and discuss it with your artist. The appointment can take up to three hours, so make sure to block out enough time in your schedule.

The actual microblading process is the shortest part of the appointment. Most of the time will be spent brow mapping and revising with your artist. The artist will mix your pigment according to your hair roots, and will swatch a bit on your skin to test for allergies and color accuracy. Pigments are mixed according to natural hair growth and skin tone. Your pigment swatch should match your root hair color, unless you direct the artist otherwise.

The artist may apply a numbing agent before or after drawing on your brows, which will likely be a lidocaine or benzocaine gel or cream. Let your artist know if you are allergic to either of these. The brow outline is drawn according to your facial measurements. There are several methods of measuring.

- Using a three-pointed hinged ruler to mark and measure your brow.
- Using thread that has been run along a sanitary eyeliner pencil or through ink.
- Using pre-made stencils to draw a brow (not recommended as brows should be custom measured).
- Using a sticker ruler that can be stuck to your forehead.

Many semi permanent makeup professionals have been trained to identify and measure your unique facial proportions using a technique called the Golden Ratio. The Golden Ratio is how your artist will be able to see and correct imperfections in your brow symmetry. The Golden Ratio is used to estimate the correct length of a brow for your face, and to find how high it should go using the brow bone as a guideline. The space between your eyebrows will be measured using the length of your eye.

Once your artist has mapped these points out, they draw a boundary that indicates how wide, long, and arched the brows should be. Then the client would then give feedback about where in the boundary they would like their brows to end. You and your artist will be deciding all aspects of your brows: thinner, shorter, flatter, etc. It is based on your personal preference and style and the ratios. Your artist is trained to identify your ratios and balance your face.

Eyebrow shapes measured correctly will be different on every client. Even identical twins! No two faces are exactly alike. Some artists use stencils, which is fine, but if you want better work, find someone who takes the time to do your measurements.

It's similar to buying a bra. You want Victoria's Secret brows, not Wal-Mart brows.

Though brow trends come and go, the right shape can really open your eyes, enhance your natural beauty, and roll back the clock by drawing attention to where it should be. Your artist should choose a brow shape that will age gracefully with time over the next few years.

Once the artist begins microblading, you should be numb. If you do feel extreme discomfort, let them know. The sound of the blade across your skin is a bit shocking and scary at first, but you'll get used to it quickly. When you see your brows for the first time, they will be the boldest they will be throughout the whole process, especially to you.

Some people say they look like Groucho Marx for a day or so afterwards, as the brows darken significantly before they scab up; but just be patient and wait the 10-15 days for them to heal. Brows will fade 20-50 percent from the initial application. So, it's hard to say if you'll like them or not at first. It's a rollercoaster healing process because the end result looks completely different from what you see initially.

What to expect during semi permanent brow healing:

Day 1- Sensitivity, swelling, a bit of bleeding

Day 2- Soreness, slight swelling, a bit of bruised feeling, heaviness

Day 3- Brows will start to look darker, swelling and soreness will be gone

Most Difficult Days
Day 4- Itching, darkening, dryness
Day 5- Itching; Scabs

Day 6- Worse itching; More scabs
Day 7- The most itchy day (for me personally); All the scabs
Day 8 through 11- Scabs will start to fall off; Color will look uneven. Don't pick your scabs.
Day 12 through 14- You can apply light makeup if your brows are healed and you are self-conscious. It is best to let them breathe, though.
Day 15 through 30- They will just get better and better every day, and you'll be so glad you were patient with the scabs. You will probably schedule a touch up appointment to perfect them around Day 30.

*****NOTE**: Older clients should understand that their healing time may be extended due to slower rates of healing.

PAIN

Pain is a big concern for many. Let me clear this up. Someone is breaking your skin open with a tiny knife. **It's not going to feel nice.** On a scale of 1-10, microblading is between a 4-6 for most. Eyeliner and lip blush discomfort are between a 5-7 for most. Even with the numbing it may be a bit uncomfortable, but if you choose the right artist, it is also quick. The actual microblading usually takes less than 30 minutes, maybe 45 minutes for machine brows.

When I microbladed my own brows, I was surprised to realize it was not terribly painful. **And I'm a bit of a pansy**. It was more irritation than pain. A client once told me it felt like 'someone was scratching a day old sunburn', and I believe that is the most accurate description. There will be minor swelling and a bit of irritation, so they might be sore, but remember that you have a hundred tiny paper cuts that are healing, and at the end, they will be beautiful!

CHAPTER SIX

AFTER MICROBLADING

After your brows are finished, you should be given a packet of instructions and some aftercare ointment. If you are not given aftercare, you can use antibiotic ointment, or Aquaphor. Your brows may ooze a clearish fluid after the procedure, not blood. This is normal. Keep gently blotting them with a clean tissue until it has stopped. Wash your brows gently with your fingers for about a week by blotting with baby soap or the provided aftercare soap. At day 5 or 6, apply the ointment. Apply just enough aftercare ointment to soften them a bit. Your brows should not be soaked to the point they are greasy or shiny. Continue with your aftercare gel or ointment until your scabs are gone, which is usually around day 11- 14. Keep in mind that your eyebrows will itch for the first 10 days as scabs form and fall away. Try your best to resist the urge to scratch them. Scratching will ruin the way your eyebrows heal. I found that gently bumping the heel of my (washed and dry) hand against them helped the itching.

Also, quite of few of my clients would come in for their touch up and their tails and arches would be extremely worn, usually in the same spots. I went full Sherlock Holmes, asking in detail about their washing and showering habits, making sure they weren't putting on makeup. Gradually, I realized they are all side or stomach sleepers, so for hours and hours of their healing process, they were rubbing their faces into a pillowcase, and basically exfoliating their scabs and yanking the pigment out of their brows right along with it!

If you are a side or stomach sleeper (or someone who frequently rolls around) stick some band aids over your ends, just for the healing - Not the sticky part, but the gauze section of the band-aid over the arches and ends. You may need two on each side. I know, I know, that looks ridiculous, but then you won't look ridiculous for a year, and won't that be the greatest?

DOS

Do **change your pillowcase** every day or two during the healing process. It keeps bacteria from building up and getting into your open brows.

Do take short showers. The steam from the shower isn't great for the pigment. Keep your face out of the direct shower stream as much as possible.

Do put on a hat and sunglasses when going outside during the healing process. **Keep the sun off your face**; your brows will heal stronger and be more vibrant.

Do **put on sunscreen after the healing process** is over. Using a high SPF sunscreen will lengthen the life of your semi permanent makeup.

Do **avoid the gym** during healing so you don't expose your brows to bacteria. Gyms are great and all, but sometimes there is nasty stuff like **staph or MRSA** that you do not want to get in your unhealed brows.

DON'TS

Don't swim in pools, hot tubs, lakes, or oceans during the healing process. There is bacteria in them and it's not great for your unhealed brows. Even the salt in ocean.

Don't get sunburned or go tanning. Avoid the sun at all costs. It will impede healing and fade the color.

Don't sweat excessively if you can help it for the duration of the healing process. You have an excuse not to work out. Take this time to stretch, do low intensity yoga, breathing exercises.

Don't pick at your scabs. Don't. Do not. Stop it. Wear a rubber band around your wrist and snap it when you start picking. I'm not kidding. I know it's hard not to, but it's so worth it.

Don't wear makeup on the brow area. Yes, I mean foundation. Yes, I mean concealer. It's just for a few days and you'll be fine.

TOUCH UP

Given that the pigment only penetrates the upper layer of the skin, over time, the strokes will start to fade gradually and may need a retouch. This is what makes semi permanent makeup so great: You can change your brow style as gradually as you would normally, but you don't have to do them constantly.

RESULTS

Skin type will ultimately determine the results of your semi permanent makeup.

Drier skin will heal the most pronounced or most 'crisp', as we say. This is true of older women with crepey skin, as well. Oily skin, due to its higher oil production, breaks down the pigment quicker. So if you have oily skin you are likely to need a touch up sooner, and then more frequently afterwards as your skin may blur the strokes over time. This is often why artists will only do combination, powder, or ombre brows on those with oily skin. Normal to dry skin typically heals the quickest and has the best results, but metabolism and age and general health have the most to do with determining how quickly you heal and how long your pigment lasts before fading.

CHAPTER SEVEN

RISKS

It is important to stress that, like other forms of tattooing, there are some risks associated with microblading. As with any procedure that involves blood, there is a risk of blood borne pathogens like Hep C or HIV. This is minimized in semi permanent makeup as all artists should use fresh gloves and most semi permanent makeup tools are individually sealed and disposable. Be sure to check that your artist complies with hygienic safety standards.

There is a small risk of allergic reaction or infection, but this rarely happens and the risk is made even smaller by following aftercare instructions and doing swatch tests at the beginning of the appointment to test for allergies. Pigments used in semi permanent makeup are subject to approval by the Food and Drug Administration as cosmetics. Good semi permanent makeup artists use FDA or European pigments since Europe currently has the strictest purity standards in the world.

Currently there is no standard board for the standalone appraisal of semi permanent makeup professionals, but there is movement to establish a Board of Microblading in the US. Choosing an artist who has been through a course in sanitation and blood-borne pathogens can help you be sure your risk is small.

The biggest takeaway here is that microblading and semi permanent makeup are new and developing, the way individual lash extensions were a few years ago. So, use your judgement! If you get a bad feeling, it's probably right. Do not be afraid to get up and leave if you feel a situation is not safe or sanitary, or an artist is making you nervous.

REMOVAL

As great as semi permanent makeup is, sometimes you won't be happy with the results. When this happens, there are a few options. If it is right after the procedure, I would suggest you wait. No matter how many times I explain the healing process, I almost always get panicked clients furiously calling or texting that are worried their brows are too dark the day after. If, after your brows have healed, the color isn't dark enough or some of your hairs strokes have faded, that is normal. Your brows may just need a touchup. Artists usually factor this in to their pricing. You can also do the opposite of the after care instructions. Sweat, go outside in the sun (don't get burned, but expose them to the sun), go for a swim, head to the sauna, wash your brows in a gentle exfoliation (read: CAREFULLY. Don't be rubbing them until they're raw, that's just not healthy, as your skin will be healing from trauma).

CHAPTER EIGHT

What is a Semi permanent Makeup Artist?

I like to think of semi permanent makeup artists like preservationists in a museum who gently repair an existing masterpiece. Using organic based pigments and small, fine needles, semi permanent makeup artists refresh a woman's natural beauty which helps them reclaim their time and energy by eliminating the need to apply traditional makeup.

When choosing any artist look at their portfolio of work. Check their Instagram, or Facebook, look through their before and after photos of healed work. Most 'after' photos are taken immediately after the procedure and look really great because the pigments are so fresh and the brows are newly groomed. These 'after' photos are not how the brows look after they have healed for fifteen days. You want to see how the brows look after this period, as it will show you how much skill the artist actually has.

Look for or request photos of prior clients weeks after their procedure. Those photos will most accurately show you the outcome you can expect, as some artists use makeup and editing to make the 'after' photos more appealing.

Semi permanent makeup artists are technically tattoo artists, but that doesn't mean they can tattoo a sunflower on your ankle. Their training or area of expertise is extremely specific. Tattoo artists' skills allow them to transition into semi permanent makeup more easily than SPMUAs can transition into creative tattooing. There are some tattoo artists that do both, and do them extremely well, but that is not always the case.

Where I used to live, I followed a local tattoo shop on Instagram that did BEAUTIFUL work and noticed that an artist from that shop had done some brows for a tattoo client. I assumed she had learned how to do semi permanent and was offering it as a package, but when I went to her profile and looked more closely, I realized she was tattooing the brows. The shape looked fine, **but she was using tattoo ink and a coil gun**. I feel for the women who had paid for this, as the brows will age poorly and if those clients ever want them removed, they will have to undergo expensive and painful laser removal on their face.

The moral of the story is, if you choose a tattoo artist to do your semi permanent makeup, make sure you check that they are using pigment, not ink, and a rotary tool or blade, not a coil gun.

CHAPTER NINE

CHOOSING AN ARTIST

Healed results are everything when choosing a semi permanent makeup artist.

Before you pick an artist, you need to do a ton of research and look at lots of before and after photos. There are too many good artists who are skilled and professional for you not to have a good experience. You may have to travel to the next town over or spend a little more, but if you are sure semi permanent makeup is what you want, it is more than worth the time, effort, and money. Look on Yelp and TripAdvisor, check Instagram and Facebook, read all the reviews to make sure you make the right decision for you.

All semi permanent makeup artists each have their own style and specialty. You may have one artist do your brows and another do your liner. If you want natural eyebrows, make sure you speak up and communicate what you want to the artist. Sometimes what you want is not possible because of your skin type or age, but you are in complete control of what goes on your face. It's hard to remember sometimes, but you can say no (politely, of course) and you can leave if you feel the surroundings are not sanitary or professional.

When the artist has suggestions on size, shape and color, you should listen, as they have a better view and more experience. They look at eyebrows all day, it's all they do, and you just pencil in your own. **(A quick note to those of you with old semi permanent or**

permanent makeup or tattoos: you have less options. You just do. If you go to an artist and need a cover up, it's likely that microblading is not a good choice for you. Take this into account and know that you can either have a combination of microblading and shading or an ombre brow.) While you have the final say, most artists are devoted and talented, and want to help you enhance the beauty you already have, and they are fairly good at it, so do not play 'back seat' artist.

I once had a client who had been a makeup artist for a little while. Looking back on this now, it's still crazy, but she stopped me mid procedure to grab my blade, and touch it to her brows to show me what to do while FaceTiming her husband. It was difficult to be polite, and after her paid touch-up appointment was over, I made it a point to never accept her as a client again. All her interference made it difficult for me to do my job, and though her brows turned out fine, I believe her results would have been better if I had been allowed to work.

There is no such thing as a free eyebrow. If they are cheap, there is a reason. You need to know that reason.

Sometimes the reason is that the artist is new to town and trying to build their business. Sometimes the reason is that they are just starting out. Be careful with cheap semi permanent makeup; sometimes it indicates you'll receive poor work. Do your research using Facebook, Google Reviews, and Instagram to find photos of artist work and reviews. Almost all artists keep their portfolio on Instagram. Semi permanent makeup is a high-end procedure and it should be priced accordingly. If you cannot afford to get proper brows, save for great ones or make do with brow product. I promise a brow pencil is much less painful than semi permanent make-up removal and far cheaper than correction.

The average cost of getting semi permanent brows differs from artist to artist, and popularity and experience drive the price up. Price doesn't necessarily determine expertise, though, and sometimes the demand, region, and number of artists in the area change the price. It is standard to pay $200-$3000 for the procedure. But if the artist is charging less than half, do some intensive research and read their reviews. The same goes for Groupon. Sometimes Groupons are a good deal, but always research the artist on Instagram and Facebook first. It will be obvious if your artist is abiding by city or state laws. Certifications and licenses required in your state will be displayed, and they should be able to give you a straight answer about their licensing.

CAUTIONS

Semi permanent makeup pigments are more regulated than tattoo inks.

Though the likelihood is small, semi permanent pigments can pose risks and complications like allergic reactions, scarring, and granulomas. You are trusting your artist with your face and your health, so take all the time to need to make sure you made the right choice.

Best of luck to you on your beauty journey!

BEFORE THE BLADE

Dearest reader,

Thank you for purchasing Before the Blade, What You Need to Know Before Getting Microblading and Semi Permanent Makeup. I know you could have picked any number of books to spend your time reading, but you picked mine and I am so thrilled and grateful.

I hope it helped you decide whether or not semi permanent makeup is for you.

If it did, it would be fantastic if you could share this book with people considering these procedures by posting the link on Facebook and Twitter.

If you enjoyed reading this book and it answered your questions, I would absolutely love to hear from you and hope that you take some time to post a review on Amazon.

Your feedback and support will help me learn, and some of your comments may even influence future edits to this book!

Please leave me a review on Amazon.

I want you to know that your review is essential for me as a new author. I need your criticism and encouragement to grow into a better teacher and writer! So, if you'd like to leave a review, all you have to do is click here and you're off to the races!

The sky is blue, and the day is yours!

In joy and sincerity,

Hannah   L.   Maruyama

AUTHOR BIO

Hannah Maruyama is the owner and master artist at Yama Studios, a semi permanent makeup studio based in Honolulu, Hawaii and the author of Before the Blade: What You Need to Know Before Getting Microblading or Semi Permanent Makeup.

It is her passion to inspire and educate everyone she can about new applications of semi permanent makeup, and she continually does intensive research about new and emerging beauty science developments.

Hannah is a painter and artist, and enjoys expressing that creativity in the Honolulu home she shares with her husband, Ryan, their uncle J., and pup Oreo.

You can follow her @yamastudios on Instagram, Facebook, Youtube, and   Twitter

BEFORE THE BLADE

Printed in Great Britain
by Amazon

22912206R00030